IRAQ WAR (2003 – PRESENT)
World Conflict Series

• • • • • • • • • • • • • • • • • • • •

Written by Nat Reed

GRADES 5 - 8
Reading Levels 3 - 4

Classroom Complete Press
P.O. Box 19729
San Diego, CA 92159
Tel: 1-800-663-3609 | Fax: 1-800-663-3608
Email: service@classroomcompletepress.com

www.classroomcompletepress.com

ISBN-13: 978-1-55319-364-7
ISBN-10: 1-55319-364-4

© 2009

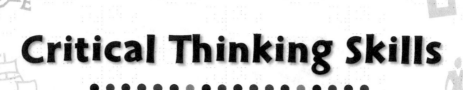

Critical Thinking Skills

Iraq War (2003 – Present)

Skills For Critical Thinking	Iraq - Desert, Oil and Saddam Hussein	The Persian Gulf War	World Terrorism	Last Moves	Operation Iraqi Freedom	The Fall of Baghdad	Aftermath	A Soldier's Story	Hands-on Activities
Chapter Questions									
LEVEL 1 — Remembering									
• List Details/Facts	✓		✓		✓		✓		✓
• Recall Information	✓	✓	✓	✓	✓	✓	✓		✓
• Match Vocabulary to Definition	✓	✓	✓	✓	✓	✓	✓	✓	
• Define Vocabulary		✓						✓	
• Sequence			✓						✓
LEVEL 2 — Understanding									
• Demonstrate Understanding	✓	✓	✓	✓	✓	✓	✓	✓	✓
• Describe	✓	✓	✓	✓	✓	✓	✓	✓	✓
• Classify			✓		✓			✓	✓
LEVEL 3 — Applying									
• Application to Own Life	✓	✓	✓	✓	✓	✓	✓		✓
• Organize and Classify Facts		✓	✓	✓		✓	✓		✓
• Infer Outcomes	✓	✓	✓	✓	✓	✓	✓	✓	
• Utilize Alternative Research Tools	✓	✓	✓	✓	✓	✓	✓	✓	✓
LEVEL 4 — Analysing									
• Distinguish Meanings	✓	✓	✓	✓	✓	✓	✓	✓	
• Make Inferences	✓	✓	✓	✓	✓	✓	✓	✓	✓
• Draw Conclusions	✓	✓	✓	✓	✓	✓	✓	✓	✓
• Identify Cause and Effect	✓	✓	✓	✓	✓	✓	✓	✓	✓
• Identify Supporting Evidence	✓	✓	✓				✓		✓
LEVEL 5 — Evaluating									
• Compile Research Information	✓	✓	✓	✓	✓	✓	✓	✓	✓
• Design and Application									✓
• Create and Construct									✓
• Imagine Alternatives			✓	✓	✓		✓	✓	✓
LEVEL 6 — Creating									
• State and Defend an Opinion	✓	✓	✓	✓	✓	✓	✓	✓	✓
• Make Recommendations		✓						✓	✓

Based on Bloom's Taxonomy

Contents

• • • • • • • • • • • • • • • • • • •

TEACHER GUIDE

- Assessment Rubric 4
- How Is Our Resource Organized? 5
- Bloom's Taxonomy for Reading Comprehension 6
- Vocabulary 6

STUDENT HANDOUTS

- Reading Comprehension
  1. Iraq – Desert, Oil and Saddam Hussein 7
  2. The Persian Gulf War 12
  3. World Terrorism 17
  4. Last Moves 22
  5. Operation Iraqi Freedom 26
  6. The Fall of Baghdad 30
  7. Aftermath 34
  8. A Soldier's Story 38

- Hands-on Activities 42
- Crossword 46
- Word Search 47
- Comprehension Quiz 48

EASY MARKING™ ANSWER KEY 50

OVERHEAD TRANSPARENCIES 55

Assessment Rubric

•••••••••••••••

Iraq War (2003 – Present)

Student's Name: _____ Assignment: _____ Level: _____

	Level 1	**Level 2**	**Level 3**	**Level 4**
Knowledge and Understanding	Demonstrates a limited understanding of content. Needs teacher assistance	Demonstrates a basic understanding of some of the content. Needs some teacher assistance	Demonstrates a good understanding of the content. Needs little teacher assistance	Demonstrates an excellent understanding of the content. No Teacher assistance needed
Inquiry and Research Skills	Able to answer questions about the text with limited effectiveness, not supported with proof from the text	Able to answer questions about the text with some effectiveness, supported with some proof from the text	Able to answer questions about the text with considerable effectiveness, supported with proof from the text	Able to answer questions about the text with a high degree of effectiveness, with excellent supporting proof from the text
Application and Making Connections	Limited application and interpretation in activities and responses, with few details	Basic application and interpretation in activities and responses, with some detail	Good application and interpretation in activities and responses, with a variety of details	Excellent application and interpretation in activities and responses, with a variety of concise details

STRENGTHS:

WEAKNESSES:

NEXT STEPS:

Teacher Guide

Our resource has been created for ease of use by both
TEACHERS and STUDENTS alike.

Introduction

The Iraq War has been a complex, multifaceted and controversial military operation which saw the United States act to topple the regime of Iraqi dictator Saddam Hussein, which US President George W. Bush saw as a threat to global peace and security. After the rapid defeat of the country's conventional military, the United States would face years of unrest and instability in Iraq, as well as varying levels of anti-war feelings and protests at home. Students will learn about the background to the region, the origins of the conflict, and the parties involved. The war, its progression and aftermath are all covered. Packed with reading passages, student activities, color overheads and fun exercises, this resource can be used effectively for whole class, small group and independent work.

How Is Our Resource Organized?

STUDENT HANDOUTS

Reading passages and **activities** *(in the form of reproducible worksheets)* make up the majority of our resource. The reading passages present important grade-appropriate information and concepts related to the topic. Embedded in each passage are one or more questions that ensure students understand what they have read.

For each reading passage there are BEFORE YOU READ activities and AFTER YOU READ activities.

*   **The BEFORE YOU READ activities** prepare students for reading by setting a purpose for reading. They stimulate background knowledge and experience, and guide students to make connections between what they know and what they will learn. Important concepts and vocabulary are also presented.

*   **The AFTER YOU READ activities** check students' comprehension of the concepts presented in the reading

passage and extend their learning. Students are asked to give thoughtful consideration of the reading passage through creative and evaluative short-answer questions, research, and extension activities.

The **Assessment Rubric** *(page 4)* is a useful tool for evaluating students' responses to many of the activities in our resource. The **Comprehension Quiz** *(page 48)* can be used for either a follow-up review or assessment at the completion of the unit.

PICTURE CUES

Our resource contains three main types of pages, each with a different purpose and use. A Picture Cue at the top of each page shows, at a glance, what the page is for.

🍎 **Teacher Guide**
*   Information and tools for the teacher

✏️ **Student Handouts**
*   Reproducible worksheets and activities

✅EZ **Easy Marking™ Answer Key**
*   Answers for student activities

EASY MARKING™ ANSWER KEY
Marking students' worksheets is fast and easy with this **Answer Key**. Answers are listed in columns – just line up the column with its corresponding worksheet, as shown, and see how every question matches up with its answer!

Every question matches up with its answer!

Bloom's Taxonomy

Our resource is an effective tool for any SOCIAL STUDIES PROGRAM.

Bloom's Taxonomy* for Reading Comprehension

The activities in our resource engage and build the full range of thinking skills that are essential for students' reading comprehension and understanding of important social studies concepts. Based on the six levels of thinking in Bloom's Taxonomy, and using language at a remedial level, information and questions are given that challenge students to not only recall what they have read, but to move beyond this to understand the text and concepts through higher-order thinking. By using higher-order skills of applying, analysing, evaluating and creating, students become active readers, drawing more meaning from the text, and applying and extending their learning in more sophisticated ways.

Our resource, therefore, is an effective tool for any Social Studies program. Whether it is used in whole or in part, or adapted to meet individual student needs, our resource provides teachers with essential information and questions to ask, inspiring students' interest, creativity, and promoting meaningful learning.

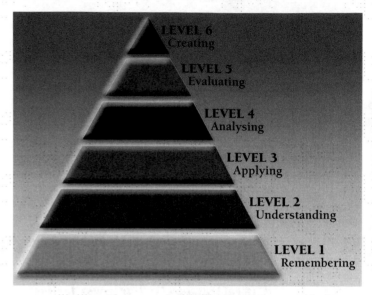

LEVEL 6 Creating
LEVEL 5 Evaluating
LEVEL 4 Analysing
LEVEL 3 Applying
LEVEL 2 Understanding
LEVEL 1 Remembering

BLOOM'S TAXONOMY: 6 LEVELS OF THINKING

Bloom's Taxonomy is a tool widely used by educators for classifying learning objectives, and is based on the work of Benjamin Bloom.

Vocabulary

acceptable	chemical weapons	inspections	outskirts	sniper
advance	civilian	inspectors	parachuted	stability
aerial assault	civilization	interior	paramilitary units	stallions
Afghanistan	coalition	invade	Pentagon	statistics
aftermath	complicated	Iran	persecute	stockpiles
airfields	conflict	Iraq	Persian Gulf War	strategy
air strike	conquer	Israel	personnel	streamed
ally	contend	Jordan	poisonous gas	Sunnis
al-Qaeda	cooperate	Kurds	Poland	surface-to-surface missiles
ambition	cultivation	Kuwait	police	suspicious
ancestor	debt	lawlessness	protective suits	tactic
apparent	desperate	loan	questionable	terrorism
Arabic	detonate	manufacturing	react	Tigris
army division	dictator	Middle East	Republican Guard	Tikrit
asset	disastrous	minority	reserves	Tommy Franks
atomic bomb	discouraged	Moslem	retreat	Tony Blair
Australia	earnest	Mosul	sabotage	topple
axis of evil	elite	motivate	Saddam Hussein	torn up
Baath Party	ethnic	occasion	Saudi Arabia	Turkey
Baghdad	Euphrates	oil	Scud missile	United Nations
Bill Clinton	expert	oil wells	Security Council	unpredictable
biological weapons	George H.W. Bush	Operation Desert Shield	seized	vaccinations
bunker	George W. Bush	Operation Desert Storm	September 11	weapons of mass destruction
bypass	Great Britain	Operation Iraqi Freedom	Shiite	widespread
campaign	grief	oppress	shock and awe	World Trade Center
casualty	guerrilla	Osama bin Laden	slant drilling	

NAME: _____

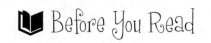

Iraq – Desert, Oil and Saddam Hussein

1. **Complete each sentence with a word from the list. Use a dictionary to help you.**

unpredictable	Cultivation	minority	Ambition
asset	persecute	civilization	reserves

a) An _____ is a valuable item that is owned.

b) A _____ is an advanced state of human society.

c) A _____ is the opposite of a *majority*.

d) To _____ is to harass or oppress because of religion, race, or beliefs.

e) A country's _____ are items that are saved or set aside.

f) _____ usually involves a desire for power, fame, wealth or honor.

g) _____ is the act of raising or growing plants.

h) If someone is _____, no one can be sure how they will act.

2. **What comes into your mind when you hear the word *Iraq* or the phrase *Middle East*?**

_____

_____

_____

NAME: _____

Iraq – Desert, Oil and Saddam Hussein

The geographical area in which the country of Iraq is located has been home to people and civilizations for countless generations. Some of the world's oldest civilizations and cities, in fact, were located in what is now Iraq. Only since 1921, however, has this land been known as "Iraq".

Euphrates River, Iraq

Iraq is located in southwest Asia and is the world's 58th largest country. It is roughly twice the size of the state of Kansas. Its population (about 27 million) is slightly larger than that of Texas. Although much of Iraq is sandy desert, it is blessed with the presence of two mighty rivers that run through the country – the **Tigris** and **Euphrates**. These rivers are major assets to farming in this region. As you might expect in a desert region, Iraq's summers are very hot – but its winters are quite cool – especially in the mountainous area to the north.

The **Arabic** people, for the most part, control Iraqi society. They make up about three-quarters of the population. Sixty percent of Iraq's population are Shiite Muslim Arabs. A minority, the Sunni Muslim Arabs, has been the group that has governed the country for most of the past 100 years. The Kurds are the third-largest group, are mostly located in the northeastern corner of the country, and for many years had been persecuted. They are also Sunni Muslims.

How might the presence of different ethnic groups and different Muslim sects spell trouble for Iraq?

_____

_____

Only about half of Iraq's very limited arable land is under cultivation. Nevertheless, many Iraqis make their living growing such crops as rice, corn, and dates. Many people in Iraq make their living in the **oil industry**. This is by far the most important industry in the country – and in the entire Middle East region. It is thought that Iraq has the second largest oil reserves in the world, buried under the sands of its deserts. It is this great wealth that has been the source of many of the terrible troubles that Iraq has gone through in the past thirty years – three major wars, and a number of bloody rebellions.

NAME: _____

Iraq – Desert, Oil and Saddam Hussein

From 1979 until 2003 Iraq was ruled by the Baath Party and its leader, **Saddam Hussein.** The Baath Party was known for its hatred of anything Western or American. Saddam Hussein was born in a small remote village, and for most of his adult life had one burning ambition - to become President of Iraq. Shortly after taking control of the country, Hussein had many of his rivals killed or imprisoned, and for the next twenty-five years he ruled the country with an iron fist.

British Soldiers pose with a portrait of Saddam Hussein, taken from a Baath Party building

How might Hussein's hatred of the West have made difficulties for his country, especially since it is Western nations that buy most of Iraq's oil?

_____

_____

It wasn't long after taking control of Iraq that Hussein led his nation into war with neighboring **Iran**. It was a terrible war that lasted for eight long years and took the lives of 200,000 Iraqi soldiers. It was also terribly expensive, and almost bankrupted the country. Soon after the end of the Iraq-Iran War, the **Kurdish tribes** in the north began an uprising. Thousands of Kurds died when Iraqi troops used poisonous gas against them.

It probably should have come as no surprise to the world when, in 1990, the unpredictable Saddam Hussein made one of the most important decisions (and greatest errors) of his life, and ordered his troops to invade the neighboring country of Kuwait, setting off the **Persian Gulf War**.

Iraq – Desert, Oil and Saddam Hussein

1. **Match the words in the box below with the correct statement.**

Kurds	Sunnis	Baath	Iran

   A [   ]   The Moslem group that has governed Iraq for much of the last century.

   B [   ]   One of Iraq's neighbors.

   C [   ]   A people living in the mountainous region of northeastern Iraq.

   D [   ]   The political party to which Saddam Hussein belonged.

2. **Put a check mark (✓) next to the answer that is most correct.**

   a) Iraq is about twice the size of:

   ○ **A.** Rhode Island
   ○ **B.** Alaska
   ○ **C.** California
   ○ **D.** Kansas

   b) The two rivers running through Iraq are:

   ○ **A.** Tigris and Euphrates
   ○ **B.** Tiger and Eucalyptus
   ○ **C.** Telus and Utica
   ○ **D.** none of the above

   c) Saddam Hussein ruled Iraq from:

   ○ **A.** 1956-2001
   ○ **B.** 1987-1999
   ○ **C.** 1979-2003
   ○ **D.** 1978-2007

Iraq – Desert, Oil and Saddam Hussein

3. **Answer each question with a full sentence.**

A) What troubles has the country of Iraq experienced during the past thirty years or so?

_____

_____

_____

B) How do you think Saddam Hussein's rule might have added to Iraq's problems?

_____

_____

_____

Research

The Middle East has been in the news almost daily for the last several years. Iraq, of course, is just one country of many making up this region of the world. Choose a nation from the list below and compile an **Information Sheet** on it. You may wish to include on the sheet information about the size of the country, its location, population, agricultural products, industry, etc. Your report should total about a half-page in length.

| Saudi Arabia | Kuwait | Iran | Israel | Syria | Jordan |

The Persian Gulf War

Answer the question in complete sentences.

1. The great Greek thinker, **Aristotle**, once said, "We make war so that we may live in peace." War, however, is a most terrible thing. Do you think it is ever right to go to war? If so, when?

    _____

    _____

    _____

2. **Match the term on the left to its definition on the right. You may use a dictionary to help you.**

1 desperate	to defeat	A
2 massive	friend	B
3 demand	having an urgent need	C
4 fabulous	a person exercising absolute power	D
5 dictator	causing great distress or injury; very unfortunate	E
6 ally	claim as a right; ask for in no uncertain terms	F
7 conquer	large, huge	G
8 disastrous	wonderful	H

The Persian Gulf War

By the summer of 1990 Saddam Hussein had grown rather desperate. He had been Iraq's president for more than ten years and for most of that time the country had been involved in a terrible war with Iran. Not only had the war cost the lives of thousands of soldiers from both countries, but it had also put Iraq seriously in debt to nations such as **Kuwait** and **Jordan**.

When the **Iraq-Iran War** finally came to an end in 1988, Saddam and his government were desperate to rebuild their shattered country. In Saddam's mind countries like Kuwait, which had supported Iraq in its war against Iran, should have been willing to forgive the massive loans they had made to Iraq. Instead, Kuwait demanded repayment. Although a tiny nation compared to Iraq and Iran, Kuwait was the fifth-largest producer of oil in the world. It was a very rich little country.

Saddam was furious. He accused Kuwait of flooding the market with too much oil, forcing the price down. This, he said, was costing Iraq millions of dollars. He then accused them of "slant drilling" by sticking long pipes under the Iraqi border and stealing his oil. Finally, in the summer of 1990 Saddam demanded $27 billion from Kuwait, and when they refused to pay, he decided to invade.

What do you suppose might have been another motive for Saddam wishing to conquer Kuwait?

_____

_____

At the time, Iraq had the fourth largest army in the world. During its war with Iran it had been well equipped with military hardware by countries such as the United States and the Soviet Union. Kuwait was no match for the mighty Iraqi military machine, and the country was conquered in a matter of days.

NAME: _____

The Persian Gulf War

The rest of the world looked on in shock. Other countries in the Middle East (such as Saudi Arabia) were afraid that the conquest of Kuwait was just a "warm-up" for Iraq's troublesome dictator. Could they be next? Saudi Arabia was the world's largest oil producer and a fabulously wealthy country. Countries such as the United States were afraid that Iraq would cut off their source of oil, driving up prices. This would have been disastrous for the economies of these countries.

What American industries do you think would have been in particular danger if the supply of oil from the Middle East had been cut off?

_____

_____

The Security Council of the United Nations, an international organization working to promote security, development, human rights, and world peace, immediately spoke out against the invasion, calling upon Iraq to withdraw all of its troops. President George H.W. Bush of the United States sent the first American troops and warplanes to the Persian Gulf. This became known as **Operation Desert Shield**.

To the surprise of a lot of world leaders, Saddam Hussein defied the order of the United Nations, and the deadline for withdrawal passed. Saddam Hussein, however, had made a serious error, for on January 16, 1991 the United States and a number of allied nations launched a massive air strike on Iraqi military targets, and the Persian Gulf War (**Operation Desert Storm**) began. It would be one of the shortest wars on record – only 42 days long, but it was also one of the most deadly. Before the six weeks were over, thousands of lives were lost and much of Kuwait was left in ruins. The Iraqis would indeed be driven from Kuwait, but Saddam Hussein would cling to power and would remain there for another twelve long years.

NAME: _____

The Persian Gulf War

1. **Complete each sentence with a word from the list. Use a dictionary to help you.**

| army | Saudi Arabia | States | Nations | Jordan | drilling |

a) After its war with Iran, Iraq was in debt to countries such as Kuwait and _____.

b) Hussein accused Kuwait of "slant _____".

c) Iraq had been equipped with military hardware by such countries as the United _____.

d) At the time of Iraq's invasion of Kuwait, it had the fourth largest _____ in the world.

e) One of Iraq's neighbors that was disturbed with the invasion of Kuwait was _____.

f) The United _____ gave the Iraqis until January 15, 1991 to leave Kuwait.

2. **Break out an atlas – or check out the internet.**
You have been introduced to a number of important countries so far in this unit. Find out the capital city for each of these countries:

a)	Iraq	
b)	Iran	
c)	Kuwait	
d)	Saudi Arabia	
e)	Jordan	

The Persian Gulf War

3. Answer each question with complete sentences.

a) Explain the meaning of the names **Operation Desert Shield** and **Operation Desert Storm**.

_____

_____

_____

b) Despite Iraq's defeat in the Persian Gulf War, why had the war's outcome not really addressed the most major problem in Iraq?

_____

_____

_____

Research

Although the **Arabs** and **Kurds** comprise the two major ethnic groups in Iraq, there are a number of smaller distinct groups as well. Examples include: Iraqi Turkmen, Assyrians, Armenians, Persians, Shabaks and Lurs.

Select <u>one</u> of these ethnic minorities and prepare a short report describing things about them that make them different or distinct. You may wish to consider such things as origins, clothing, diet, culture, language, etc.

Your report should be about a half-page in length.

NAME: _____

World Terrorism

1. **Using the words in the box, write each word beside its meaning.**

stockpiles	manufacture	contend	suspicious
motivate	axis	destruction	ethnic

A [_____] belonging to the cultural, racial, religious, or linguistic traditions of a people

B [_____] to struggle, dispute, compete

C [_____] to cause or prompt

D [_____] to suspect or distrust

E [_____] to make or produce

F [_____] to destroy or demolish

G [_____] a supply for future use

H [_____] an alliance of two or more nations

2. **In the upcoming chapter a character named *Osama bin Laden* is mentioned. What do you already know about this man?**

_____

_____

_____

_____

_____

World Terrorism

The Middle East area has long been a troubled region of the world. It is home to a number of different languages, ethnic groups and religions. For generations many of the countries and peoples there have been ill-treated by Western nations – even before the discovery of oil in the region. In some ways the discovery of oil has only added to the problems faced by the people living in this mostly desert region – they now have to face foreigners trying to take advantage of them, as well as rulers motivated by greed and personal ambition.

World Trade Center in New York City on 9/11

Although the world was no stranger to acts of terror, the events on September 11, 2001 made the entire world sit up and take notice. On that dark day two planes were flown into the World Trade Center in New York City, another into the Pentagon in Washington D.C., and a fourth plane was forced down in Pennsylvania. Two thousand nine hundred ninety-three people lost their lives, and an international terrorist organization known as **al-Qaeda** was deemed responsible.

How do you think these acts of terrorism contributed to America's decision to attack Iraq?

_____

_____

Ten years had passed between the end of **Persian Gulf War** (which ended in 1991) and the events of September 11, 2001. In those ten years the United Nations had ordered Iraq to get rid of its programs aimed at developing poisonous gases and nuclear bombs. United Nations inspectors had been sent to Iraq to check sites that looked suspicious, but the Iraqi government did not cooperate in the way the inspectors would have liked.

In 1998 US President Bill Clinton ordered a series of air strikes against targets where it was believed **weapons of mass destruction** were being made. After this, no inspections were conducted for four years, a fact that made the United States very uneasy. Was Iraq making an atomic bomb? At the time no one knew for sure.

World Terrorism

The United States and other Western nations knew that **Osama bin Laden** was the leader of the terrorist group that carried out the 9/11 attacks. Bin Laden was a millionaire from Saudi Arabia whose headquarters was believed to be in Afghanistan.

However, President George W. Bush made it known that Saddam Hussein and his Iraqi government were suspected of supporting terrorist groups such as al-Qaeda. In a 2002 speech Bush called Iraq a member of the "axis of evil" – along with Iran and North Korea. He also began to publicly call for military action to be taken against Iraq. He told people in the United States and around the world that he believed Iraq was manufacturing **weapons of mass destruction** (poisonous gas, nuclear bombs) and that Saddam Hussein was supporting al-Qaeda. The American government said that they had evidence that Iraq had large stockpiles of chemical weapons and was actively seeking materials to make nuclear weapons.

Do you think President Bush's reasons for going to war were convincing?

_____

_____

Many countries in Europe and elsewhere in the world did not support America's call for military action. Countries such as France, Germany, and Russia suggested that more time should be given for the weapons inspectors to go through the questionable sites in Iraq.

Iraq finally let the weapons inspectors back into the country in November 2002. After three months of inspections no weapons of mass destruction had been found. However President Bush and his government still did not consider Hussein to be completely cooperative, and the path to war seemed unstoppable.

World Terrorism

1. **Circle** the word **TRUE** if the statement is TRUE or **Circle** the word **FALSE** if it is FALSE.

   a) The Middle East has been a relatively peaceful area of the world for centuries.

   TRUE   **FALSE**

   b) Altogether four planes were hijacked during the events of 9/11.

   TRUE   **FALSE**

   c) It is believed that Osama bin Laden masterminded the events of 9/11.

   TRUE   **FALSE**

   d) Despite the protests of the United Nations, no weapons inspectors were ever allowed into Iraq.

   TRUE   **FALSE**

   e) In 1998 President Bill Clinton ordered a series of air strikes on Iraq.

   TRUE   **FALSE**

   f) It is believed that Osama bin Laden's headquarters was in Afghanistan.

   TRUE   **FALSE**

2. **What were the two main reasons given by President George W. Bush for invading Iraq?**

   1. _____

   2. _____

World Terrorism

3. Answer each question with a complete sentence.

a) Why were some countries (like France and Germany) not so sure that the Americans should have invaded Iraq when they did?

_____

_____

_____

b) President Bush called Iraq and two other countries an "axis of evil". Which two other countries did he include in this description, and what do you think he meant by this statement?

_____

_____

_____

_____

Research

George W. Bush

Not many presidents of the United States could make the claim that their father was also a former president. President George W. Bush <u>could</u> make that claim. His father, George H.W. Bush was president from 1989-1993. George W. Bush became president in 2001 and served until 2009. His presidency will be remembered for the events of 9/11 and the Iraq War.

Your task is to write a brief biography of **President George W. Bush**. Be sure to include important facts regarding his personal and public life and his accomplishments as president.

Your report should be about a half-page in length.

Last Moves

1. **Imagine that you are an Iraqi citizen at the time that the American forces are preparing to invade your country. Describe how you might feel and what preparations you would make for such an event.**

_____

_____

_____

2. **Match each word to its definition. You may use the dictionary to help you.**

1 conflict	all right, satisfactory, tolerable	A
2 aftermath	an alliance	B
3 acceptable	something that results or follows from an event	C
4 personnel	entrance to take possession or overrun	D
5 invasion	a person that is harmed or killed as a result of some act or event (often in wartime)	E
6 coalition	fight, battle or disagreement	F
7 casualty	a body of persons employed in an organization	G

Last Moves

The main ally of the United States during this crisis was **Great Britain**. During the difficult days of the war and its aftermath, Britain and its Prime Minister Tony Blair worked hand-in-hand with the Americans.

Tony Blair

The military leaders of the United States asked the leadership of the country of **Turkey** for permission to launch attacks against Iraq from their territory. Turkey had long been an ally of the United States, and as a Moslem country, the Americans believed that involving Turkey would make the attack on Iraq more acceptable to other Moslem countries in the region. However, Turkey refused to give their permission, and the United States was forced to use Kuwait as the place from which they would launch the invasion.

Even though the United States and Britain did not have the complete support of the United Nations, they began gathering together a coalition force in Kuwait. The United Nations urged the Americans to give the weapons inspectors more time to complete their work in Iraq. By then the American military force in Kuwait numbered nearly 250,000 personnel. There were also about 45,000 British personnel, 2,000 Australian troops, 1,300 Spanish soldiers, 500 Danish soldiers and 200 Polish soldiers. Pressing on the coalition military leaders was the fact that if they were going to invade Iraq they would have to do it before the summer weather got too hot. Temperatures in Iraq can soar to more that 120°F (50°C) in the summer.

Why do you think more countries did not support the Americans in this war?

_____

_____

On March 19, 2003 the United States launched an air strike in an effort to kill Saddam Hussein. The Americans believed that Hussein was attending a meeting in a bunker just outside Baghdad. It turned out, though, that there was no bunker in this location, and a number of civilian casualties resulted from the bombardment.

The next day, on March 20th, the invasion of Iraq, codenamed **Operation Iraqi Freedom**, and led by General Tommy Franks, had begun.

Last Moves

1. Circle the word **TRUE** if the statement is TRUE **or** Circle the word **FALSE** if it is FALSE.

   a) The main ally of the United States at the time was France.

   TRUE　　　FALSE

   b) The Prime Minister of Great Britain in 2003 was Tony Blair.

   TRUE　　　FALSE

   c) The United States asked Syria if they could use their country to attack Iraq from.

   TRUE　　　FALSE

   d) The United States was grateful for the full support of the United Nations Security Council.

   TRUE　　　FALSE

   e) The Americans comprised more than three-quarters of the total coalition forces at the start of the war. (Get out your calculators!)

   TRUE　　　FALSE

2. **Number the events from ❶ to ❺ in the order they happened.**

   a) A coalition force of nearly 300,000 armed forces personnel gathers in Kuwait.

   b) As war looms, Great Britain is the biggest supporter of the U.S.

   c) Operation Iraqi Freedom begins on March 20, 2003.

   d) An air strike to kill Saddam Hussein is launched, but fails.

   e) The U.S. asks Turkey if they could use their country to attack Iraq from.

After You Read 📖

Last Moves

3. Answer each question with a complete sentence.

a) Why did the United Nations Security Council not want the coalition forces to take action against Iraq?

_____

_____

b) Why do you think hot weather would be a problem for the military?

_____

_____

c) What do you think the Americans hoped might happen if they were able to kill Saddam Hussein before launching the invasion?

_____

_____

Research

The reading mentions that the commander of the coalition forces was **General Tommy Franks**, the head of U.S. Central Command. Using resources in your school library or on the internet, find out more about this man. Record at least five important details about his life and career. You may wish to record personal data, or information on his military career – or a mix of the two.

You report should be about a half-page in length.

NAME: _____

Operation Iraqi Freedom

1. **With a straight line, connect each word on the left with its meaning on the right.**

A	campaign	to stop	1
B	expert	to put down or suppress.	2
C	earnest	chief officer or leader	3
D	awe	to move or bring forward	4
E	topple	a military operation	5
F	prevent	a person with a special skill	6
G	expect	sincere	7
H	commander	feeling of admiration or fear	8
I	advance	to conquer or defeat	9
J	oppress	to look forward to	10

2. **The coalition's military invasion of Iraq was given the name Operation Iraqi Freedom. Do you feel this is a suitable name? Defend your answer.**

_____

_____

3. **The coalition forces felt that the Iraqi people would welcome them as liberators. Do you feel there was a good chance of this happening? Why or why not?**

_____

_____

Operation Iraqi Freedom

The military strategy for **Operation Iraqi Freedom** was different from the strategy for the Persian Gulf War. Instead of a long bombing campaign before the invasion, the air attack and invasion were planned for the same time. The Americans also used a much smaller military force for this war. Some military experts even felt that the invasion force was too small to win such a war. These experts knew that although the Iraqi army had grown weaker over the years, it still numbered about 400,000 men.

After the bombing attack that was meant to kill Saddam Hussein, the Iraqi army began firing surface-to-surface missiles at coalition bases in Kuwait and setting fire to oil wells in southern Iraq.

On the night of March 21, 2003, coalition forces streamed into southern Iraq and a massive aerial assault was launched against the capital city of Baghdad, destroying many important military targets. These air attacks were referred to as a "shock and awe" campaign. This alone, though, did not topple Hussein's government.

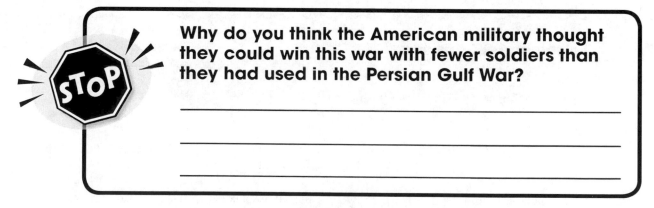

STOP

Why do you think the American military thought they could win this war with fewer soldiers than they had used in the Persian Gulf War?

_____

_____

_____

The coalition forces quickly captured two airfields in western Iraq to prevent them from launching Scud missile attacks against Israel – as they had in the Persian Gulf War in 1991.

The strategy of the coalition commanders was to bypass most of the major cities in the south and focus on taking Baghdad, the capital city and the center of Saddam Hussein's authority in the country. Coalition armies would first be met by cheering crowds, but also quickly came to face massive civil disorder and chaos.

Operation Iraqi Freedom

1. Fill in each blank with the correct word from the reading.

a) A lengthy _____ campaign before the invasion of Iraq was not planned by the coalition leaders this time.

b) The military planners of Operation Iraqi Freedom planned the land invasion and the _____ attack for the same time.

c) The Americans also had a much _____ force compared to that in the 1991 Persian Gulf War.

d) It was thought that the Iraqi army numbered about _____ men.

e) The first coalition bombing attack was an attempt to kill _____.

f) The war began on _____, 2003.

2. (Circle) the correct answers.

a) The air attack on Baghdad was called:

steel rain   shock and awe   punishment alley   freedom fighters

b) The coalition forces were afraid the Iraqis would fire these into Israel:

Scud missiles   Patriot missiles   stealth bombs   hand grenades

c) Coalition strategy was to bypass the smaller cities and concentrate on:

Damascus   Karbala   Dahuk   Baghdad

Operation Iraqi Freedom

3. Answer each question with complete sentences.

a) Why do you think the Iraqis set fire to their own oil wells?

_____

_____

_____

b) Why do you think the Americans were so concerned about Israel staying out of the war?

_____

_____

_____

c) Why do you think coalition leaders expected the conflict to end quickly and without much effort? Why didn't it?

_____

_____

_____

Research

The Prime Minister of Great Britain at this time was **Tony Blair**. It was Prime Minister Blair who provided much in the way of military assistance and moral support to the Americans in this war. He was Prime Minister from 1997 to 2007. Blair is the British Labor Party's longest-serving Prime Minister and the only person to have led the Labor Party to three consecutive general election victories.

Write a brief report (about one-half page) about Prime Minister Blair's life and accomplishments.

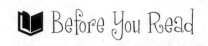 Before You Read

NAME: _____

The Fall Of Baghdad

1. **Complete each sentence with a word from the list. Use a dictionary to help you.**

outskirts discouraged	desperate elite	protective retreat	parachuted interior

a) The Iraqi army began to _____ as the coalition forces approached the city.

b) The Republican Guard divisions were the _____ soldiers in Saddam Hussein's army.

c) My parents bought a house on the _____ of Chicago.

d) I think she was very _____ after losing her fifth straight tennis match.

e) The soldiers were required to wear _____ suits when entering the lab.

f) After being locked in the hot building all day, my cat became so _____ that she began to drink from the toilet.

g) After checking the outside of the apartment building, the inspectors moved into the _____ .

h) The 14th Airborne Division _____ into the mountains surrounding the city.

2. **Albert Einstein** once said about war: "I know not with what weapons World War III will be fought, but World War IV will be fought with sticks and stones." What do you think the great scientist meant?

_____

_____

_____

_____

The Fall of Baghdad

The commanders of the coalition forces thought that the Iraqi army's strategy would be to keep on retreating before making a final desperate stand in Baghdad – Iraq's capital city and Saddam Hussein's headquarters. Six divisions of the elite Iraqi **Republican Guard** were stationed on the outskirts of Baghdad (a **division** usually contains between ten and twenty thousand soldiers). Another division of Republican Guard was stationed on the interior of the city.

As the coalition forces closed in on Baghdad the fear grew that Saddam Hussein might use chemical or biological weapons. Vaccinations against smallpox and anthrax were given to the coalition soldiers, and many were given protective suits to wear.

It turned out that Saddam Hussein and his army commanders had a different strategy in mind. Instead of using the famed Republican Guard, **paramilitary units** from the southern part of the country were put into battle (a paramilitary unit refers to *a group of civilians trained and organized in a military fashion*). In addition to the danger these units posed to the coalition armies, the presence of these paramilitary units in the southern part of the country also discouraged local people from welcoming the coalition forces. It therefore became necessary for the Americans and their allies to defeat these paramilitary units before continuing on to Baghdad. British forces led an operation in southern Iraq in the city of Basra, taking control of the city after a fight with Iraqi military and paramilitary forces.

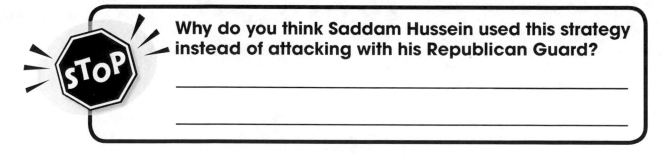

Why do you think Saddam Hussein used this strategy instead of attacking with his Republican Guard?

_____

_____

It was also important for coalition forces to take control of the northern part of the country. The **Kurds**, who lived in this area, had already promised the Americans support for the invasion. Over 1,000 American soldiers parachuted into this region and captured an important airfield. This then allowed the coalition forces to fly in tanks and other weapons for use in the north. Kurdish and coalition forces were then able to capture **Mosul**, the largest city in northern Iraq.

In early April, only a couple of weeks after the start of the war, coalition forces approached Baghdad and seized the airport. Hussein's grip on power was gone. The beginning of the end was now in sight.

NAME: _____

The Fall of Baghdad

1. Circle the word **TRUE** if the statement is TRUE **or** Circle the word **FALSE** if it is FALSE.

   a) The commanders of the coalition forces thought the Iraqi army would make a final stand at Baghdad.

       TRUE   **FALSE**

   b) Iraq's elite army divisions were known as the *Republican Guard*.

       TRUE   **FALSE**

   c) A division in the army usually contains between one and two thousand soldiers.

       TRUE   **FALSE**

   d) The coalition forces were worried that Saddam Hussein might use biological weapons against them.

       TRUE   **FALSE**

   e) A paramilitary unit is one that is composed entirely of paratroopers.

       TRUE   **FALSE**

   f) The Kurds in the north had promised to fight with the coalition armies.

       TRUE   **FALSE**

2. **Put a check mark (✓) next to the answer that is most correct.**

   a) The largest city in northern Iraq is:

       ○ **A.** Schwarzkopf
       ○ **B.** Mosul
       ○ **C.** Damascus
       ○ **D.** Kenogami

   b) Saddam Hussein's headquarters was in:

       ○ **A.** Mosul
       ○ **B.** Washington D.C.
       ○ **C.** Baghdad
       ○ **D.** he didn't have a headquarters

The Fall of Baghdad

3. Answer each question with a complete sentence.

a) How did the use of Iraqi paramilitary units in the south complicate the plans of the coalition forces?

_____

_____

_____

b) Why were the American soldiers parachuted into northern Iraq?

_____

_____

_____

Research

Saddam Hussein relied to a great extent on members of the **Republican Guard** to defend himself and his regime from the invading forces. Research and record several facts about the Republican Guard that you consider interesting and important. Your report should be about a half-page in length.

Aftermath

1. **Using the words in the box, write each word beside its meaning.**

tactic	**complicated**	**apparent**	**stability**
civilian	**widespread**	**ancestor**	**sabotage**

[_____]   **a)** a person from whom one is descended

[_____]   **b)** a person who is not in the military or the police

[_____]   **c)** occurring in many places or among many persons

[_____]   **d)** to undermine

[_____]   **e)** clear, evident

[_____]   **f)** a plan or procedure

[_____]   **g)** to continue without change; permanence

[_____]   **h)** difficult, complex

2. **a)** Can you predict what difficulties there might have been in governing Iraq after the war was over?

_____

_____

_____

_____

Aftermath

U.S. Marines entered the capital city of Baghdad on April 9, 2003, facing little resistance. One of the first things they did was to help Iraqi civilians tear down a huge statue of Saddam Hussein in the city square. A few days later the city of Tikrit was captured by coalition forces. This was important because Tikrit was the ancestral home of Saddam Hussein.

With the fall of the Iraqi government, the problem of looting soon became widespread. The Americans did not have enough troops to properly police the country, and lawlessness became an especially serious problem in cities such as Baghdad. While many Iraqis were glad to see Saddam Hussein gone from power, his former supporters attacked power stations, oil pipelines and bridges in hopes of sabotaging the Americans' hold on the country. Coalition forces also soon became the target of suicide bombers and snipers.

Why do you think the Iraqis chose these tactics to fight the coalition?

_____

_____

On May 1, 2003 President George W. Bush declared an end to major combat operations in Iraq and stated that "an ally of al-Qaeda had been defeated". What was disturbing to many people in the months that followed was the discovery that at least two of the major reasons President Bush had used for going to war were proven wrong. No weapons of mass destruction were ever found in Iraq, and there were no clear links between Hussein and the terrorist group al-Qaeda.

The aftermath of invading another country and removing its government has proven difficult. Iraq is a complicated country with different ethnic groups and multiple religious groups who have strong feelings about each other. The people in charge of rebuilding

NAME: _____

Aftermath

the nation and its government have faced years of guerrilla warfare and unrest. Even Iraqis who were glad to see Saddam Hussein removed from power have resented foreign troops patrolling their streets. Car bombings and shootings created even more instability. Saddam Hussein was captured in December of 2003 and executed after a trial in December 2006. Yet even this did not bring an end to the demonstrations, car bombings and unrest.

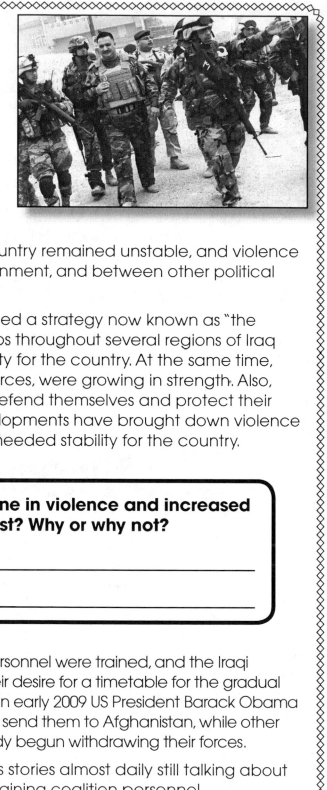

In 2005 Iraqis celebrated after the success of elections for a new constitution and for their first democratically elected government. Still, the country remained unstable, and violence aimed at coalition forces, at the new Iraqi government, and between other political and religious groups and factions continued.

In early 2007, President George W. Bush announced a strategy now known as "the surge", increasing the number of American troops throughout several regions of Iraq in order to provide increased stability and security for the country. At the same time, the Iraqi government, and its army and police forces, were growing in strength. Also, militias made up of ordinary citizens looking to defend themselves and protect their communities were forming. Together, these developments have brought down violence and have helped to provide some desperately needed stability for the country.

Do you think the decline in violence and increased stability in Iraq can last? Why or why not?

_____

_____

By September of 2008, over 545,000 Iraqi security personnel were trained, and the Iraqi government and parliament had begun noting their desire for a timetable for the gradual withdrawal of the coalition forces from the country. In early 2009 US President Barack Obama promised to withdraw some forces from Iraq and to send them to Afghanistan, while other coalition countries, such as Great Britain, had already begun withdrawing their forces.

Iraq remains a country in some turmoil, with news stories almost daily still talking about protests, bombings, and the deaths of some remaining coalition personnel.

After You Read 📖

Aftermath

1. Fill in each blank with the correct word from the reading.

a) The capture of the city of _____ was important because it was Hussein's ancestral home.

b) _____ became widespread with the fall of the Iraqi government.

c) The coalition forces did not have enough troops to _____ the whole country.

d) Hussein's former supporters attacked power stations, pipelines and _____.

e) Coalition forces also became the target of suicide bombers and _____.

f) No links were found between Iraq and the terrorist group _____.

g) No weapons of mass _____ were ever found.

2. Although it was upsetting that President Bush was wrong about Iraq possessing weapons of mass destruction, how might it also have been a relief to learn this?

_____

_____

3. a) What do you think the goal of Saddam Hussein's supporters would be in blowing up power stations, etc. – even after it looked like they had lost the war?

_____

_____

b) How do you think you would feel if you were to wake up every morning to the sight of soldiers from another country patrolling the streets of your town or city? Why do you think you would you feel this way?

_____

_____

Research

The terrorist organization **Al-Qaeda** is mentioned several times in this unit. It has been on the front pages of American newspapers for the last several years. What exactly though is al-Qaeda? How did it get its start? Who are the leaders? What are its goals?

Investigate al-Qaeda using resources in your school library or on the internet. Prepare a half-page report summarizing what al-Qaeda is and what it is trying to accomplish, and by what means.

 NAME: _____

A Soldier's Story

1. The expression '**torn up**' can refer to an emotional state of someone very upset or in real distress. Write a sentence using the expression 'torn up'.

_____

_____

2. **Synonyms** are words with similar meanings. Use the context of the sentences below to help you choose the best synonym for the underlined word in each sentence. If you need help, consult a dictionary.

a) <u>Statistics</u> don't give the total picture of what happens in combat.

A. numbers   **B.** newspapers   **C.** reporters   **D.** correspondents

b) No one expected the suitcase to <u>detonate</u>.

A. leave   **B.** explode   **C.** circulate   **D.** age

c) My cousin was trained as a <u>sniper</u> in the war.

A. driver   **B.** cook   **C.** marksman   **D.** artillery operator

d) Dr. Jones raises <u>stallions</u> at his ranch in Kansas.

A. bison   **B.** billy goats   **C.** yaks   **D.** horses

e) No one expected her to <u>react</u> the way she did.

A. curtsy   **B.** scream   **C.** flinch   **D.** respond

f) I think he expected it to be a memorable <u>occasion</u>.

A. party   **B.** event   **C.** convention   **D.** conference

     Iraq War (2003 – Present) CC5509

📖 Reading Passage

A Soldier's Story

The Iraq War affected the lives of thousands of people – not only those of Iraqis, but also of American, British, Australian, Polish and other coalition soldiers and their families. It changed forever the lives of many soldiers who went to war in Iraq, and the lives of their families and loved ones - wives, children, parents.

Since the war began in 2003 over 4000 American soldiers have died in combat in Iraq. In addition there have been approximately 30,000 Americans wounded and over 300 combat deaths in the armies of other coalition nations.

What do these cold, hard figures mean though? What do they mean to the families of the soldiers who died or were badly wounded? Here are just three soldiers who gave their lives in the Iraq conflict:

- **Sgt Mark P. Adams**: 24 years old, killed when a homemade bomb detonated during combat operations against enemy forces in Saqlawiyah, Iraq

- **Capt. Paul C. Alaniz**: 32 years old, died when the CH-53E Super Stallion helicopter he was in crashed near Ar Rutbah in western Iraq

- **2nd Lt. Tracy Lynn Alger**: 30 years old, died of wounds suffered when a roadside bomb detonated near her vehicle in Shubayshen, Iraq

Tracy Alger was one of many female military personnel to fight in Iraq. Why do you think women weren't allowed into combat situations in most other wars historically?

_____

_____

What is it like to lose a loved one in a war? Soldier Timothy VanDruff lost his stepson, Lucas, to a sniper in Iraq. Here are Timothy's thoughts as he flew home to tell his wife the news: "The flight from California to Kansas City was rough because I did not know how I was going to react when I saw my wife, knowing she was torn up because she had just lost her son. We had just lost our son. I have never been that sad before. You expect to go home and it be a happy occasion. This time, it wasn't."

Thousands of people across the United States, Iraq and other countries have had to face such terrible feelings of grief after losing a loved one in Iraq. Was it all worth it? How would the families of these soldiers answer such a question?

NAME: _____

A Soldier's Story

1. Put a check mark (✓) next to the answer that is most correct.

a) Since the war began in 2003, how many Americans have died in combat in Iraq?

- ○ **A.** over 4,000
- ○ **B.** over 10,000
- ○ **C.** over 20,000
- ○ **D.** over 100,000

b) How was Sergeant Adams killed?

- ○ **A.** a vehicle accident
- ○ **B.** by a sniper
- ○ **C.** by 'friendly fire'
- ○ **D.** by a homemade bomb

c) In the first paragraph of this chapter four coalition countries are mentioned. Which of the following countries was not a member of the coalition?

- ○ **A.** Poland
- ○ **B.** Australia
- ○ **C.** Canada
- ○ **D.** Great Britain

d) Not including Americans, about how many coalition soldiers were killed in Iraq?

- ○ **A.** over 500
- ○ **B.** over 300
- ○ **C.** over 1,000
- ○ **D.** None

e) In what city did Timothy VanDruff's wife live?

- ○ **A.** Kansas City
- ○ **B.** Topeka
- ○ **C.** New York City
- ○ **D.** Los Angeles

A Soldier's Story

2. Answer each question with complete sentences.

a) What lessons do you think the coalition countries may have learned from their experiences in Iraq?

_____

_____

_____

b) *"A thing is not necessarily true because a man dies for it."*
                                                        - Oscar Wilde

What do you think about this quote from Oscar Wilde? Why might the soldiers who died in Iraq have been willing to give their lives for this cause?

_____

_____

_____

Research

Pat Tillman was a professional football player who volunteered for service in the Iraq War. Unfortunately he was later killed in a '*friendly fire*' incident in Afghanistan. His sacrifice made a great impression on many people, and he is remembered as a hero today.

Investigate the life of Pat Tillman using either your school library or the internet. Find out at least five interesting facts about him and prepare a report of at least a half-page in length.

Post It on a Poster

For generations posters have been an effective way of publicizing events, advertising products, and making announcements. Posters have come a long way in the last hundred years. Early posters were only in black ink and rarely featured any artwork. Posters today are in full color and feature all kinds of imaginative, eye-catching graphics and fonts.

Your task is to create an imaginative, colorful and effective poster. The poster should in some way be tied in with our study of Iraq and its recent history. You may consider one of the following ideas, or come up with one of your own:

- A recruitment poster for an Iraqi company. Select or make up a company of your choice (perhaps in the oil industry, or in police services) and design a poster intended to attract workers to Iraq. You should probably note that while the pay and benefits are good, the risks may be quite high.

- A *Wanted Dead or Alive* poster for a war criminal (ex. Saddam Hussein before his capture, one of his lieutenants still at large, a terrorist, etc.).

- A poster whose purpose is to attract tourists to Iraq. The country still boasts many wonderful historical sites – and accommodations and meals are very reasonably priced.

- A poster advertising one of Iraq's historical sites (ex. Babylon, Saddam Hussein's Palace, etc.).

Be sure your poster is informative, attractive and colorful. It should feature enough information to make it useful. It should also include a picture.

Where in the World...

A number of countries were mentioned in this study. For this activity you will probably need a few good resources (maybe an atlas, an almanac, an encyclopedia, the internet). This exercise is meant to be fun and to increase your general knowledge of the Middle East.

1. **a)** *Lesson Four* mentions that the coalition forces wanted to launch their attack from **Turkey**. Turkey has an area of 302,535 square miles (783,562 square kilometers). Is Turkey larger or smaller than the state of Alaska?

   _____

   b) **Turkey** has a population of approximately 72 million people. How does this compare to Iraq? Which country has the greater population?

   _____

2. **Poland** was mentioned as a country that contributed soldiers to the coalition army. Poland is not a country of the Middle East. Which continent is Poland located on?

   _____

3. Iraq's capital city **Baghdad** has a population of almost six million people. Circle the two other Iraqi cities below which have a population of over one million.

   Al-Kut   **Arbil**   **Al-'Amarah**   **Mosul**   **As-Samawah**

4. Iraq was locked in a long, bloody war with its neighbor, Iran.

   • Which country is larger, Iraq **or** Iran? _____

   • The _____ Sea is located to the north of Iran.

5. What six countries border Iraq?

   _____   _____   _____

   _____   _____   _____

A Poet's Soul

The poet doesn't invent. He listens.

\- Jean Cocteau

Many songs and poems have been written over the years describing both the horrors of war and the reasons why people will lay down their lives for a just cause. One very famous song from the American Civil War of the 1860s was written by Frederick Root, called "Just Before the Battle, Mother", which spoke of the sacrifice that many soldiers were willing to make for a cause they believed in. Here is a portion of the lyrics:

Just before the battle, mother,
I am thinking most of you,
While upon the field we're watching
With the enemy in view.
Comrades brave are 'round me lying,
Filled with thoughts of home and God
For well they know that on the morrow,
Some will sleep beneath the sod.

CHORUS:
Farewell, mother, you may never
Press me to your breast again,
But, oh, you'll not forget me, mother,
If I'm numbered with the slain.

Hark! I hear the bugles sounding,
'Tis the signal for the fight,
Now, may God protect us, mother,
As He ever does the right.
Hear the "Battle-Cry of Freedom,"
How it swells upon the air,
Oh, yes, we'll rally 'round the standard,
Or we'll perish nobly there.

You have the choice of <u>one</u> of the following two tasks.

TASK A. Find a poem or set of lyrics with a "war" theme. It can be a protest song (i.e. "Blowing in the Wind" by Bob Dylan), or a poem or song that speaks of the horrors or the glory of battle. Copy the lyrics onto a sheet of paper and write a paragraph describing your reaction to the song / poem.

TASK B. Write your own poem expressing your feelings on war, or one which tells a story about someone's experiences in wartime.

Artistic Flair

For this hands-on activity you have a **menu of options**. Choose one of the menu items below:

A. A Comic Strip

This activity is especially for students with an artistic flair or who love comic books! Your topic can be the Iraq War in general, or you may choose to focus on one aspect of it (i.e. the life of Saddam Hussein). The first step is to decide on the length of your comic strip (6 to 12 frames is suggested). Next consider what events you will include. A quick sketch of the comic strip should first be drawn in a **storyboard format** before a final, good copy is attempted. The strip should include a title, dialog and color. It should be neat and imaginative.

B. A Detailed Picture or Diorama

Do either a detailed picture <u>or</u> a diorama of some aspect of the Iraq War. Possible subjects *might* include an oil well; Saddam Hussein's palace or military bunker in Baghdad; a weapon of war; one of the coalition military personnel in uniform.

C. Adding to Your Poem

If you completed the previous activity **(Hands-On Activity 3)** you now have an opportunity to add to the overall effect of the poem and its presentation. Supplement the poem's *presentation* with a picture or other suitable visual tools which capture the poem's theme. The final product should be suitable for posting on a classroom or school bulletin board.

Crossword Puzzle!

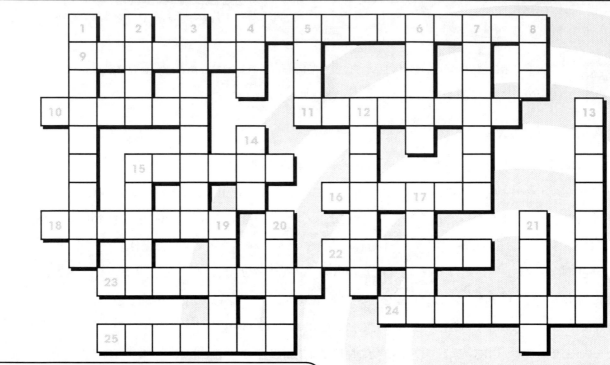

Word List

Blair	dictator	invasion	rotate
casualty	DNA	missiles	Scud
Clinton	end	net	security
contest	Franks	Operation	taste
cream	grin	Persian	trade
crown	Hussein	Poland	united
destruction	ignore	Putin	

Across

4. Weapons of mass _____.

9. _____ Gulf War.

10. Coalition commander General Tommy _____.

11. A ruler with absolute power.

15. European country that was part of the coalition.

16. Joined.

18. Competition.

22. To revolve or spin.

23. Raid or incursion by another country.

24. The act of defending.

25. Saddam _____.

Down

1. _____ Iraqi Freedom.

2. Smile.

3. Large weapons that are shot at a target.

4. Abbreviation for *Deoxyribonucleic Acid*.

5. A missile fired by Iraq in the Persian Gulf War.

6. Ice _____.

7. Not paid attention to.

8. A tool used by fishermen.

12. Former President Bill _____.

13. One wounded or killed in battle.

14. Final.

15. Russian leader.

17. Swap.

19. A sense.

20. Worn by a king or queen.

21. Former Prime Minister of Great Britain.

NAME: _____

Word Search

Find all THIRTY words in the Word Search. Words are written horizontally, vertically, diagonally, and some even backwards.

ambition	Bush	destruction	Kurds	motivate	sniper
asset	civilization	ethnic	Kuwait	persecute	stockpiles
Baghdad	coalition	guerrilla	manufacture	Poland	suspicious
Blair	contend	Hussein	minority	reserves	Turkey
Britain	cultivation	Iraq	Moslem	Saddam	unpredictable

C	T	U	R	K	E	Y	N	O	I	T	A	V	I	T	L	U	C
M	I	N	O	R	I	T	Y	Q	W	E	R	A	T	Y	U	I	I
A	S	V	D	F	G	H	E	T	U	C	E	S	R	E	P	R	O
K	S	N	I	P	E	R	H	J	K	L	Z	S	X	C	A	V	B
M	U	N	B	L	V	C	C	I	N	H	T	E	X	Q	C	M	B
P	S	R	C	X	I	Z	S	D	F	G	H	T	J	K	L	A	L
O	P	C	D	A	S	Z	D	B	R	I	T	A	I	N	A	N	E
L	I	O	S	S	D	F	A	G	H	J	K	L	Q	W	E	U	L
A	C	N	K	J	H	G	G	T	G	F	D	S	Q	W	E	F	B
N	I	T	F	G	H	H	N	O	I	T	I	L	A	O	C	A	A
D	O	E	D	D	F	U	G	G	H	O	H	H	J	V	B	C	T
Z	U	N	A	X	C	V	S	B	N	M	N	M	A	S	B	T	C
X	S	D	M	A	D	D	A	S	S	D	F	G	H	U	L	U	I
M	O	T	I	V	A	T	E	S	E	D	F	G	S	D	A	R	D
T	Z	X	C	V	B	N	M	A	S	I	S	H	S	S	I	E	E
I	S	A	L	L	I	R	R	E	U	G	N	S	D	F	R	S	R
A	S	D	D	F	G	H	N	O	I	T	I	B	M	A	S	S	P
W	D	E	S	T	R	U	C	T	I	O	N	H	J	K	L	K	N
U	P	O	I	U	Y	T	R	E	S	E	V	R	E	S	E	R	U
K	M	O	S	L	E	M	E	S	E	L	I	P	K	C	O	T	S

NAME: _____

Comprehension Quiz

 30

Part A

 8

Circle the word **TRUE** if the statement is TRUE **or** Circle the word **FALSE** if it is FALSE.

1. Much of the land in Iraq is sandy desert.

   TRUE   **FALSE**

2. Saddam Hussein's political party was called the *Strident People's Party*.

   TRUE   **FALSE**

3. Iraq had been involved in a long war with Syria.

   TRUE   **FALSE**

4. The Persian Gulf War happened because of Iraq's invasion of Kuwait.

   TRUE   **FALSE**

5. The organization **al-Qaeda** took credit for the terrorist incidents in America on September 11, 2001.

   TRUE   **FALSE**

6. The U.S. wanted to launch their attacks on Iraq from the country of Turkey.

   TRUE   **FALSE**

7. The United States accused Iraq of manufacturing weapons of mass destruction.

   TRUE   **FALSE**

8. **General Norman Schwarzkopf** was the commander of the coalition forces during the Iraq War of 2003.

   TRUE   **FALSE**

Part B

Circle the three countries below that were a part of the coalition. 3

   Canada   **Poland**   **Australia**   **France**   **Russia**   **Great Britain**

SUBTOTAL: **/11**

Part C   # Comprehension Quiz

Answer the questions in complete sentences.

1.   What were the two main reasons President Bush gave for invading Iraq?

_____

_____

_____   ④

2.   The **Republican Guard** was a concern to the coalition forces. Explain why.

_____

_____   ②

3.   Why did some countries not support America's decision to invade Iraq?

_____

_____   ②

4.   What immediate problem developed in cities such as Baghdad after the fall of Saddam Hussein and the Iraqi government?

_____

_____   ④

5.   What was the "shock and awe" campaign?

_____

_____   ③

6.   Describe why it has been so difficult for coalition forces stationed in Iraq since the war ended?

_____

_____

_____   ④

SUBTOTAL: /19

1.

a) asset

b) civilization

c) minority

d) persecute

e) reserves

f) Ambition

g) Cultivation

h) unpredictable

2.

Answers will vary.
(i.e. War, terrorism, Saddam Hussein.)

(7)

1.

A Sunnis

B Iran

C Kurds

D Baath

2.

a) D

b) A

c) C

(10)

3.

A) Wars with Iran and Kuwait and internal rebellions.

B) Answers will vary. (i.e. He showed favoritism to his own people and persecuted the Kurds, as well as leading the country into a couple of devastating wars.)

(11)

1.

Answers will vary

2.

1. C

2. G

3. F

4. H

5. D

6. B

7. A

8. E

(12)

1.

a) Jordan

b) drilling

c) States

d) army

e) Saudi Arabia

f) Nations

2.

a) Baghdad

b) Tehran

c) Kuwait City

d) Riyadh

e) Amman

(15)

3.

a) Shield was to protect the other countries in the area. Storm was the attack on Iraqi forces.

b) Answers will vary. (i.e. Hussein was still in power.)

(16)

3.

a) They wanted to give the weapons inspectors more time.

b) The extreme heat is hard on personnel and equipment.

c) Answers will vary. (i.e. Perhaps the Iraqis would no longer want to fight.)

(25)

1.

a) **FALSE**

b) **TRUE**

c) **FALSE**

d) **FALSE**

e) **TRUE**

2.

1st-b

2nd-e

3rd-a

4th-d

5th-c

(24)

1.

Answers will vary

2.

1. F

2. C

3. A

4. G

5. D

6. B

7. E

(22)

3.

a) They wanted the weapons inspectors to have more time.

b) Iran and North Korea. Answers will vary. (i.e. He was making a comparison with the Axis of WW2.)

(21)

1.

a) **FALSE**

b) **TRUE**

c) **TRUE**

d) **FALSE**

e) **TRUE**

f) **TRUE**

2.

The Iraqis were making weapons of mass destruction. Saddam Hussein was an ally of al-Qaeda.

(20)

1.

A ethnic

B contend

C motivate

D suspicious

E manufacture

F destruction

G stockpiles

H axis

2.

Answers will vary. (i.e. A terrorist from Saudi Arabia, living in hiding, believed responsible for 9/11.)

(17)

© CLASSROOM COMPLETE PRESS

Iraq War (2003 – Present) CC5509

3.

a) It delayed the coalition forces' advancement on Baghdad.

b) To capture an airfield so they could fly in tanks and other equipment.

1.

a) **TRUE**

b) **TRUE**

c) **FALSE**

d) **TRUE**

e) **FALSE**

f) **TRUE**

2.

a) ⊘ B

b) ⊘ C

1.

a) retreat

b) elite

c) outskirts

d) discouraged

e) protective

f) desperate

g) interior

h) parachuted

2.

Answers will vary. (i.e. World War III will destroy civilization.)

3.

a) They knew the Americans would soon be taking the wells over and wanted to prevent this from happening.

b) If Israel entered the war other Arab nations might have entered on the side of Iraq.

c) Answers will vary

1.

a) bombing

b) air

c) smaller

d) 400,000

e) Saddam Hussein

f) March 21

2.

a) shock and awe

b) Scud missiles

c) Baghdad

1.

A. 5

B. 6

C. 7

D. 8

E. 9

F. 1

G. 10

H. 3

I. 4

J. 2

2.

Answers will vary

3.

Answers will vary. (i.e. Saddam Hussein was hated by most Iraqis. Some people would see them as foreign troops invading their country.)

1.

a) Smaller. (Alaska's area is 663,267 sq mi)

b) Turkey. Iraq has a population of about 27 million

2. Europe

3. Mosul, Arbil

4. Iran, Caspian

5.
Iran
Jordan
Kuwait
Saudi Arabia
Syria
Turkey

(43)

2.

a) Answers will vary

b) Answers will vary

(41)

1.

a) A

b) D

c) C

d) B

e) A

(40)

---

1. Answers will vary. (i.e. She was torn up at the funeral of her brother.)

2.

a) A

b) B

c) C

d) D

e) D

f) B

(38)

1.

a) Tikrit

b) Looting

c) police

d) bridges

e) snipers

f) al-Qaeda

g) destruction

2. Answers will vary. (i.e. If there were Hussein might have fired them at the coalition forces. It might indicate that other countries like Iraq also don't have this capability yet.)

3.

a) Answers will vary. (To create instability so the coalition forces would leave).

b) Answers will vary

(37)

1.

a) ancestor

b) civilian

c) widespread

d) sabotage

e) apparent

f) tactic

g) stability

h) complicated

2.

a) Answers will vary. (i.e. It would be difficult due to the different factions in the country as well as the destruction of property caused by the war.)

(34)

Across

4. destruction
9. Persian
10. Franks
11. dictator
15. Poland
16. united
18. contest
22. rotate
23. invasion
24. security
25. Hussein

Down

1. Operation
2. grin
3. missiles
4. DNA
5. Scud
6. cream
7. ignored
8. net
12. Clinton
13. casualty
14. end
15. Putin
17. trade
19. taste
20. crown
21. Blair

Word Search Answers

Part A

1. TRUE
2. FALSE
3. FALSE
4. TRUE
5. TRUE
6. TRUE
7. TRUE
8. FALSE

Part B

Australia
Great Britain
Poland

1. He said Iraq had weapons of mass destruction. Iraq was said to be supporting the terrorist organization al-Qaeda.

2. The Republican Guard were the elite divisions of the Iraqi army.

3. They wanted to give the weapons inspectors more time in Iraq.

4. Looting, lawlessness.

5. Aerial bombing of Baghdad.

6. Sabotage, bombings, snipers.